50 POP TUNES FOR FLUTE GRADED

Published by
Wise Publications
14-15 Berners Street, London W1T 3LJ, UK.

Exclusive Distributors:
Music Sales Limited
Distribution Centre, Newmarket Road,
Bury St Edmunds, Suffolk IP33 3YB, UK.
Music Sales Corporation
257 Park Avenue South, New York, NY 10010, USA.
Music Sales Pty Limited
20 Resolution Drive, Caringbah, NSW 2229, Australia.

Order No. AM1004729
ISBN 978-1-78038-568-6
This book © Copyright 2012 Wise Publications,
a division of Music Sales Limited.

Edited by Jenni Norey.
Music processed by Camden Music.
Printed in the EU.

Your Guarantee of Quality
As publishers, we strive to produce every book to
the highest commercial standards.
This book has been carefully designed to minimise awkward
page turns and to make playing from it a real pleasure.
Particular care has been given to specifying acid-free, neutral-sized
paper made from pulps which have not been elemental chlorine bleached.
This pulp is from farmed sustainable forests and
was produced with special regard for the environment.
Throughout, the printing and binding have been planned to ensure
a sturdy, attractive publication which should give years of enjoyment.
If your copy fails to meet our high standards,
please inform us and we will gladly replace it.

www.musicsales.com

WISE PUBLICATIONS
part of The Music Sales Group

London / New York / Paris / Sydney / Copenhagen / Berlin / Madrid / Hong Kong / Tokyo

GRADING NOTES

The pieces in this book have been carefully graded according to
various criteria such as rhythmic complexity, phrasing, tempo, key, range, etc.
Look for the number of stars for each piece to give you
an idea of the approximate playing level.
All musicians have particular strengths and weaknesses,
so the grading offered here should be taken as a suggestion only.

Generally, pieces with one star have simple rhythms,
straight forward phrasings and few difficult intervals;
essentially diatonic and in easier keys.

Pieces with two stars will have more challenging passages,
perhaps containing more rhythmic complexity,
more advanced key signatures and possibly explore a wider
range on the instrument.

Three-star pieces may include chromaticism,
challenging articulation and more advanced positioning.
Read through rhythms and keys before playing, and check for
time-signature changes and correct phrasing.

All About Tonight
(Pixie Lott)

Words & Music by Brian Kidd, Thomas James & Tebey Ottoh

The A Team
(Ed Sheeran)

Words & Music by Ed Sheeran

Apologize
(OneRepublic)

Words & Music by Ryan Tedder

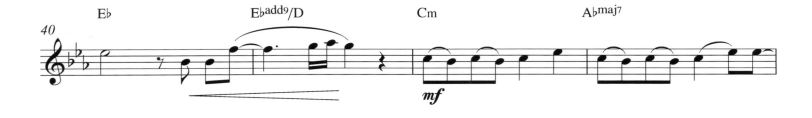

Bad Boys
(Alexandra Burke)

Words & Music by Alex James, James Busbee, Larry Summerville, Lauren Evans & Melvin Watson

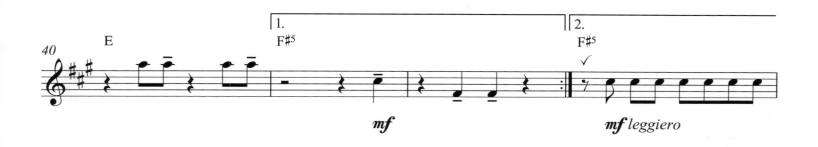

Beautiful Day
(U2)

Words by Bono. Music by U2

Bad Romance
(Lady Gaga)

Words & Music by Stefani Germanotta & RedOne

With confidence ♩ = 119

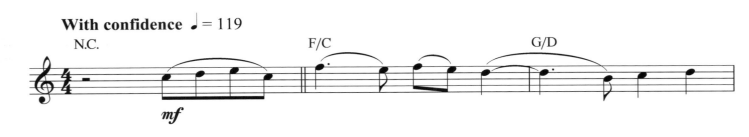

Chasing Cars
(Snow Patrol)

Words & Music by Gary Lightbody, Nathan Connolly, Tom Simpson, Paul Wilson & Jonathan Quinn

Bedshaped
(Keane)

Words & Music by Tim Rice-Oxley, Tom Chaplin, Richard Hughes & James Sanger

Bleeding Love
(Leona Lewis)

Words & Music by Ryan Tedder & Jesse McCartney

gradual cresc.

Broken Strings
(James Morrison)

Words & Music by James Morrison, Fraser T. Smith & Nina Woodford

26

Chasing Pavements
(Adele)

Words & Music by Adele Adkins & Eg White

Cry Me Out
(Pixie Lott)

Words & Music by Pixie Lott, Mads Hauge, Phil Thornalley & Colin Campsie

Don't Stop Believin'
(Journey)

Words & Music by Steve Perry, Neal Schon & Jonathan Cain

The Climb
(Joe McElderry)

Words & Music by Jessica Alexander & Jon Mabe

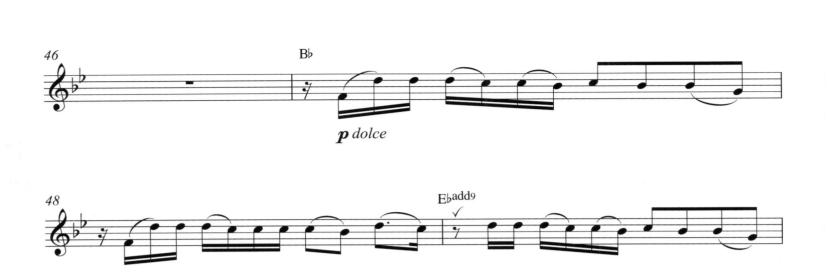

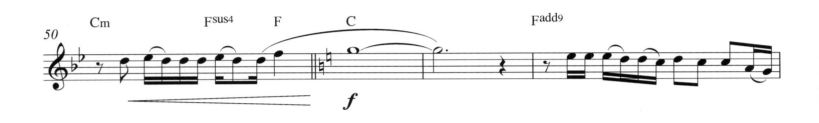

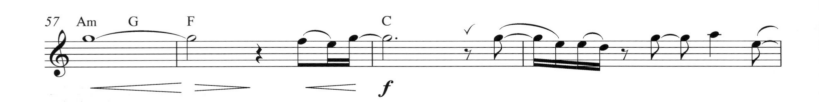

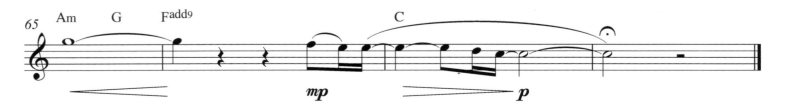

Every Teardrop Is A Waterfall
(Coldplay)

Words & Music by Chris Martin, Guy Berryman, Jon Buckland, Wil Champion & Brian Eno

The Fear
(Lily Allen)

Words & Music by Lily Allen & Greg Kurstin

Fireflies
(Owl City)

Words & Music by Adam Young

Lightly, with a bounce ♩ = 90

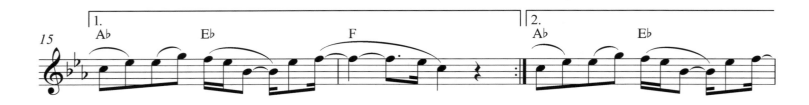

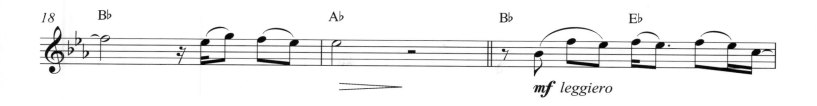

Fight For This Love
(Cheryl Cole)

Words & Music by Steve Kipner, Wayne Wilkins & Andre Merritt

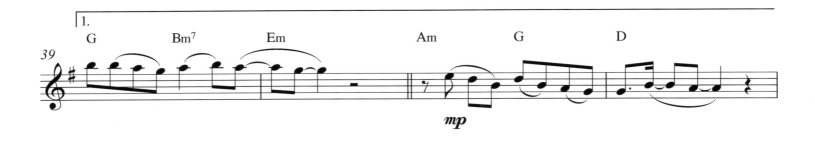

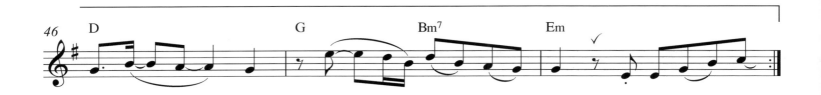

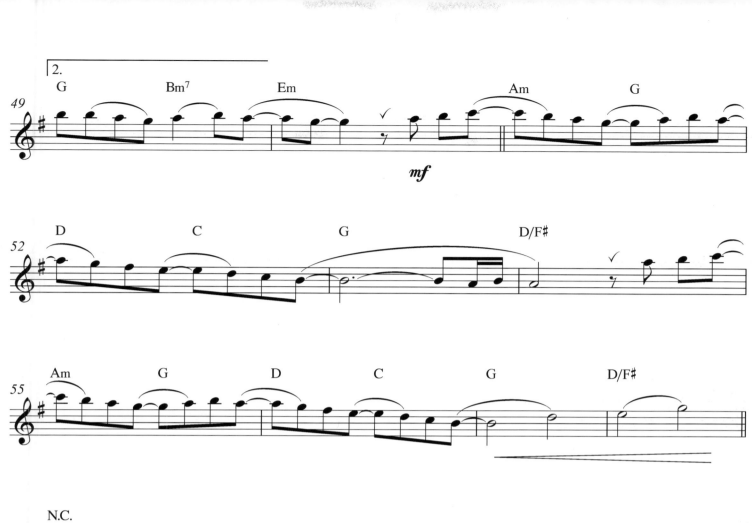

Repeat to fade

Fix You
(Coldplay)

Words & Music by Guy Berryman, Chris Martin, Jon Buckland & Will Champion

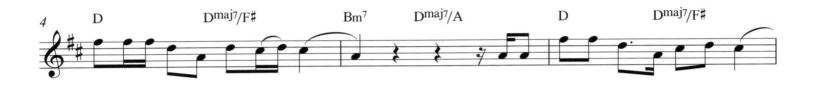

rall.

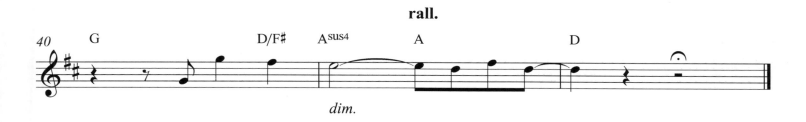

dim.

Glad You Came
(The Wanted)

Words & Music by Wayne Hector, Steve Mac & Ed Drewett

Grenade
(Bruno Mars)

Words & Music by Philip Lawrence, Peter Hernandez, Christopher Brown, Ari Levine, Claude Kelly & Andrew Wyatt

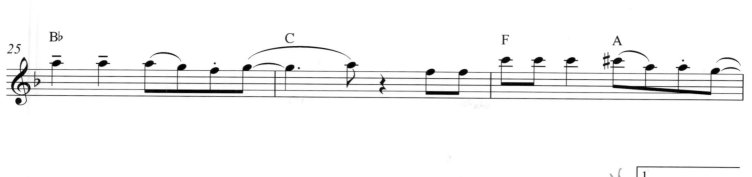

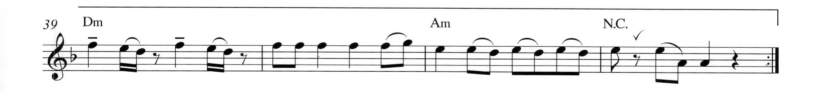

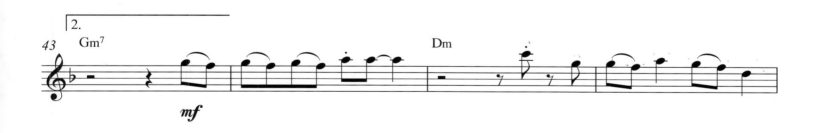

54

Forget You
(Cee-Lo Green)

Words & Music by Thomas Callaway, Philip Lawrence, Peter Hernandez, Ari Levine & Christopher Brown

Hallelujah
(Alexandra Burke)

Words & Music by Leonard Cohen

Halo
(Beyoncé)

Words & Music by Ryan Tedder, Beyoncé Knowles & Evan Bogart

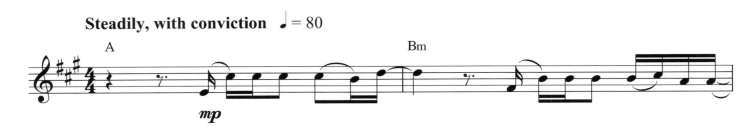

Human
(The Killers)

Words by Brandon Flowers. Music by Brandon Flowers, Dave Keuning, Mark Stoermer & Ronnie Vannucci

If I Were A Boy
(Beyoncé)

Words & Music by Tobias Gad & Britney Carlson

Is It Any Wonder?
(Keane)

Words & Music by Richard Hughes, James Sanger, Tim Rice-Oxley & Tom Chaplin

Jar Of Hearts
(Christina Perri)

Words & Music by Christina Perri, Drew Lawrence & Barrett Yeretsian

Jealousy
(Will Young)

Words & Music by Will Young, James Eliot & Jemima Stilwell

Leave Right Now
(Will Young)

Words & Music by Francis Eg White

Just Dance
(Lady Gaga)

Words & Music by Aliaune Thiam, Stefani Germanotta & Nadir Khayat

Dance beat ♩ = 118

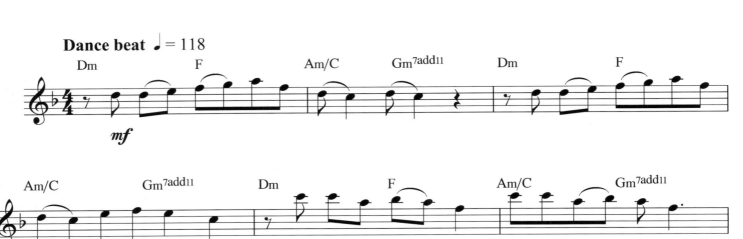

Last Friday Night
(Katy Perry)

Words & Music by Max Martin, Lukasz Gottwald, Bonnie McKee & Katy Perry

Lost
(Michael Bublé)

Words & Music by Michael Buble, Alan Chang & Jann Richards

rall.

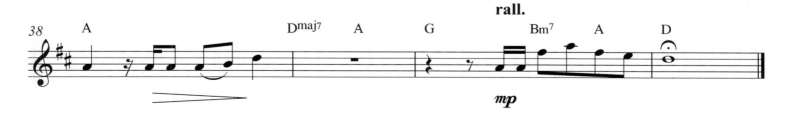

mp

Love Goes Down
(Plan B)

Words & Music by Benjamin Drew, Eric Appapoulay, Richard Cassell & Tom Goss

Love Song
(Sara Bareilles)

Words & Music by Sara Bareilles

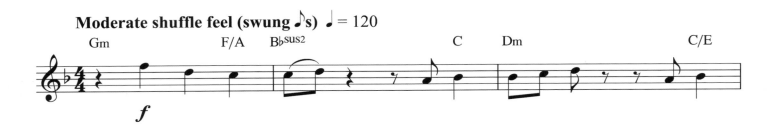

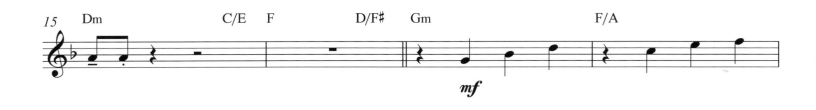

Make You Feel My Love
(Adele)

Words & Music by Bob Dylan

No Air
(Jordin Sparks)

Words & Music by Harvey Mason, Damon Thomas, James Fauntleroy, Erik Griggs & Steven Russell

Love Story
(Taylor Swift)

Words & Music by Taylor Swift

94

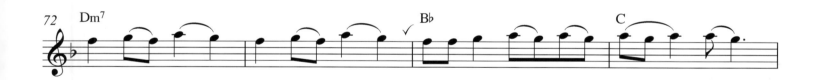

cresc. poco a poco

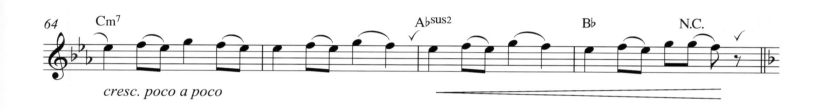

Poker Face
(Lady Gaga)

Words & Music by Stefani Germanotta & Nadir Khayat

Rule The World
(Take That)

Words & Music by Mark Owen, Gary Barlow, Jason Orange & Howard Donald

Run
(Leona Lewis)

Words & Music by Gary Lightbody, Jonathan Quinn, Mark McClelland, Nathan Connolly & Iain Archer

Russian Roulette
(Rihanna)

Words & Music by Shaffer Smith & Charles Harmon

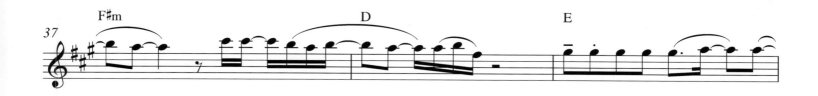

Rolling In The Deep
(Adele)

Words & Music by Adele Adkins & Paul Epworth

Shine
(Take That)

Words & Music by Mark Owen, Gary Barlow, Stephen Robson, Jason Orange & Howard Donald

Somewhere Only We Know
(Keane)

Words & Music by Tim Rice-Oxley, Tom Chaplin & Richard Hughes

Take A Bow
(Rihanna)

Words & Music by Mikkel Eriksen, Tor Erik Hermansen & Shaffer Smith

Someone Like You
(Adele)

Words & Music by Adele Adkins & Daniel Wilson

Viva La Vida
(Coldplay)

Words & Music by Guy Berryman, Jon Buckland, Will Champion & Chris Martin

You Raise Me Up
(Westlife)

Words & Music by Brendan Graham & Rolf Løvland

Warwick Avenue
(Duffy)

Words & Music by James Hogarth, Aimee Duffy & Francis Eg White